Eagle Ray

Shark and Young

Snapper

Hogfish

Cod

Yellowfin Tuna

Southern Flounder

Box Fish

Moray Eel

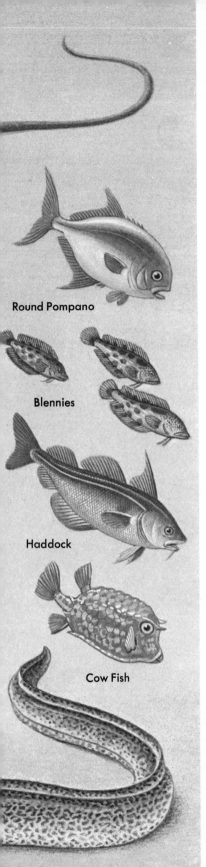

Round Pompano

Blennies

Haddock

Cow Fish

FISHES

AND HOW THEY LIVE

by GEORGE S. FICHTER

illustrated by RENE MARTIN

and JAMES GORDON IRVING

GOLDEN PRESS 🦅 NEW YORK

© Copyright 1960, 1958, 1956 by Golden Press, Inc. All rights reserved, including the right of reproduction in whole or in part in any form. Designed and produced by Artists and Writers Press, Inc. Printed in the U.S.A. by Western Printing and Lithographing Company. Published by Golden Press, Inc., Rockefeller Center, New York 20, N. Y. Published simultaneously in Canada by The Musson Book Company, Ltd., Toronto.

Library of Congress Catalog Card Number 61-5225

What Is a Fish?

Men became interested in fishes centuries ago—and we are just as much interested in them today. Prehistoric man sought fishes for food, and he soon devised spears, hooks, nets, and traps for making his catches. Today, fishes are one of our most important food resources, and many modern inventions, such as airplanes and radar, are used by commercial fishermen to help them in taking their harvests. About 20 million tons of fish are caught every year, and nearly all of these are taken from the waters of the northern hemisphere.

Fishes are one of the world's most important foods. Nearly 50 billion pounds of fish are harvested annually. They are easily digested and are an excellent source of protein, vitamins A and D, and minerals.

Long ago, man also learned that catching fish can be fun. Now fishing ranks as our most popular sport.

Many people enjoy keeping fishes as pets in an aquarium at home. Others visit the large live-fish exhibits in cities. And an increasing number of people are taking up the sport of skin diving where they meet fishes face to face in their watery world.

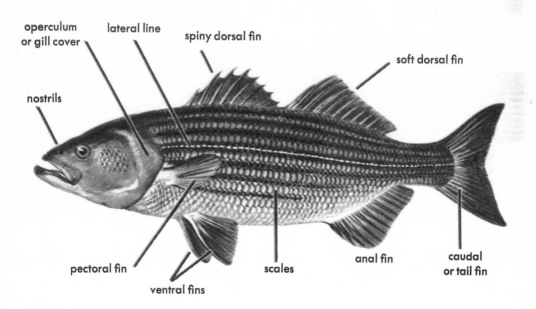

operculum or gill cover   lateral line   spiny dorsal fin   soft dorsal fin   nostrils   pectoral fin   ventral fins   scales   anal fin   caudal or tail fin

PARTS OF A FISH

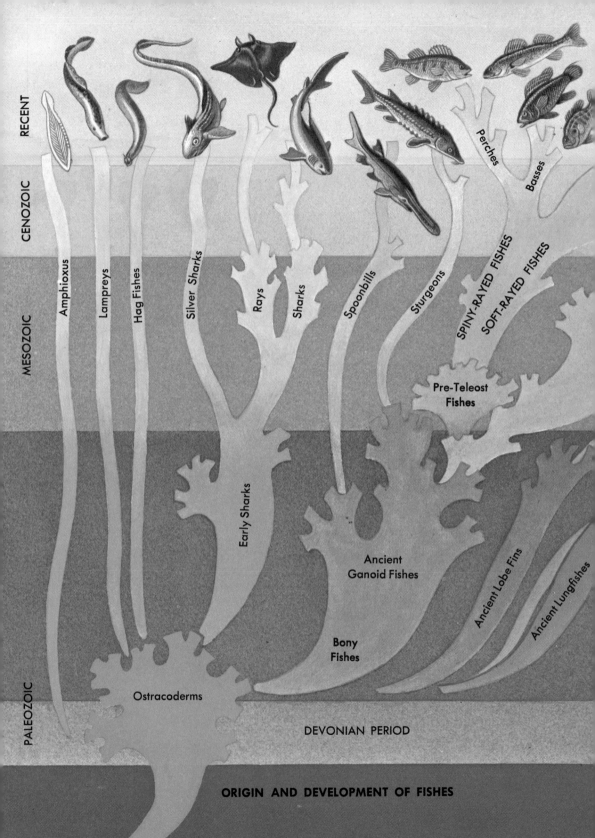

RECENT

CENOZOIC

MESOZOIC

PALEOZOIC

Amphioxus

Lampreys

Hag Fishes

Silver Sharks

Rays

Sharks

Spoonbills

Sturgeons

Perches

Basses

SPINY-RAYED FISHES

SOFT-RAYED FISHES

Pre-Teleost
Fishes

Early Sharks

Ancient
Ganoid Fishes

Ancient Lobe Fins

Ancient Lungfishes

Bony
Fishes

Ostracoderms

DEVONIAN PERIOD

ORIGIN AND DEVELOPMENT OF FISHES

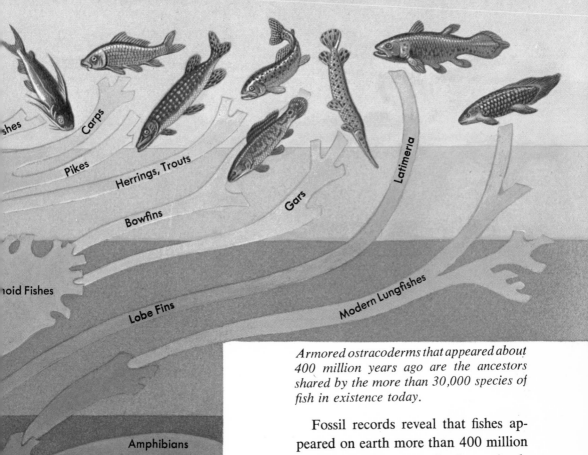

shes

Carps

Pikes

Herrings, Trouts

Bowfins

Gars

Latimeria

oid Fishes

Lobe Fins

Modern Lungfishes

Amphibians

Armored ostracoderms that appeared about 400 million years ago are the ancestors shared by the more than 30,000 species of fish in existence today.

So a fish means different things to different people. One man may think of a fish as a way to make his living. Another may consider it as the fun at the end of his fishing line. A housewife looks at a fish as the main course for a fine meal, while an engineer marvels at the fish's sleek lines of design.

Fish scientists, or ichthyologists, describe a fish as a cold-blooded animal that has a backbone; it lives in the water, breathes by means of gills, and has fins and scales. This describes the typical fish, of course.

Fossil records reveal that fishes appeared on earth more than 400 million years ago. They were the first animals with backbones.

Those primitive fish-like creatures, called ostracoderms, were covered with a heavy armor of horny plates and overlapping scales. Near the top of their heads were three eyes, and many of them are believed to have had inside their skulls special nerve organs that could produce electric shocks. They had no jaws and only poorly developed fins. Ostracoderms did live in water — in fresh-water streams, incidentally — and they breathed by means of gills. They also had a backbone, although it was made of a tough tissue called cartilage, rather than of true bone.

9

Our modern fishes — and there are more than 30,000 kinds—evolved from fishes of this sort. Three main groups have developed. First are the lampreys and hagfishes,direct offshoots from those ancient ostracoderms. Both are slim and eel-like in body shape. They have no jaws or scales or paired fins. Second are the sharks and rays. They have skeletons of cartilage and tooth-like scales imbedded in their skins. Most of our present-day fishes, however, have skeletons of bone. They are the third group—the *bony fishes*. To this group belong the bass, herring, salmon, catfish, mackerel, tarpon—the kinds of fishes that generally come to mind when we think of a fish.

Fishes range in size from the tiny Philippine goby fish, which may measure only half an inch in length when full grown, up to giant whale sharks, which may grow to be more than 50 feet long. While it may require as many as 15,000 goby fish to weigh one pound, a single whale shark can weigh more than 15 tons! Its egg alone measures a foot long. Between these extremes there are fishes of nearly every size, shape, and color.

The huge, harmless whale shark is the largest of all fishes. It has distinctive checkered markings, and inhabits all the warmer seas of the world.

The Shapes of Fishes—
a Clue to Where They Live

Salt-water seas cover about 72 percent of the earth's surface. In addition, there are numerous fresh-water lakes and streams on the land areas. With all this water in the world, fishes should have no trouble finding places to live. Yet many species are limited to a certain kind of water and to a particular area in that water.

Some kinds of fishes, for example, can live only in salt water. Others are confined to fresh water. A few kinds can live in either fresh or salt water, and fewer still divide their lives between the two, living for a while in each.

There are fishes that live in the cold seas at the earth's polar regions, but the greatest number and variety are found in warmer waters nearer to the equator. Some fishes spend their lives swimming near the surface; others are found in dark ocean waters two miles deep. Some kinds live only in cold fresh-water streams, while others thrive in hot springs where the temperature of the water is seldom below 100 degrees Fahrenheit.

The shape of a fish is often a clue to the sort of place in which it lives. Those that have spindle-shaped bodies, such

Although three-quarters of the earth is covered by water, many fishes can live only in one small area that contains water of a particular temperature and depth.

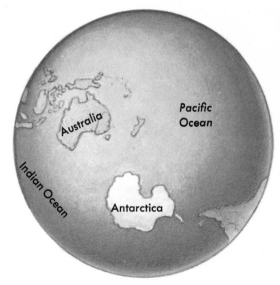

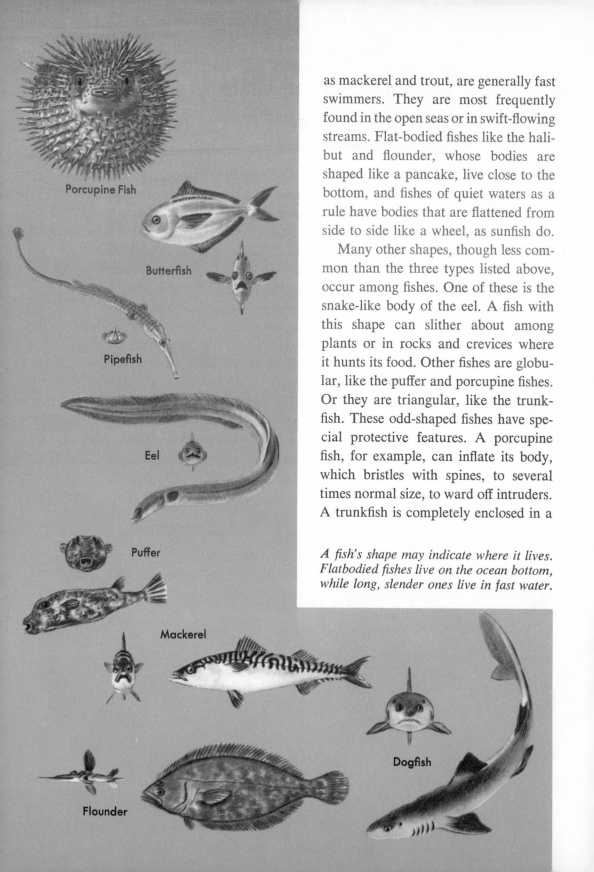

as mackerel and trout, are generally fast swimmers. They are most frequently found in the open seas or in swift-flowing streams. Flat-bodied fishes like the halibut and flounder, whose bodies are shaped like a pancake, live close to the bottom, and fishes of quiet waters as a rule have bodies that are flattened from side to side like a wheel, as sunfish do.

Many other shapes, though less common than the three types listed above, occur among fishes. One of these is the snake-like body of the eel. A fish with this shape can slither about among plants or in rocks and crevices where it hunts its food. Other fishes are globular, like the puffer and porcupine fishes. Or they are triangular, like the trunkfish. These odd-shaped fishes have special protective features. A porcupine fish, for example, can inflate its body, which bristles with spines, to several times normal size, to ward off intruders. A trunkfish is completely enclosed in a

A fish's shape may indicate where it lives. Flatbodied fishes live on the ocean bottom, while long, slender ones live in fast water.

Porcupine Fish

Butterfish

Pipefish

Eel

Puffer

Mackerel

Dogfish

Flounder

Puffers can inflate their bodies to several times normal size, to confuse or frighten attackers.

rigid, shell-like outer covering; only its fins and tail are movable.

Many of the deep-sea fishes have weird shapes. The fins of the angler fish, to illustrate, have become long, tentacle-like organs, and at their tips there are "lights" that glow in the black waters of the deep sea to attract fishes.

Sea horses have fringed fins and distorted bodies, covered with bony plates. While a sea horse is a strange sight to behold when it is out of its en-vironment, it is hard to see among the waving, feathery seaweeds where it normally lives. The little sargassum fish is an even better example of protective form and color. It is virtually invisible in its natural surroundings.

Male angler fish are dwarfs compared to their mates. Early in their lives they fasten themselves to a female's body, and then grow attached there. The tissues of the two fish fuse, and the males degen-erate into a mass consisting almost en-

The tiny male anglerfish attached to the underside of the larger female is parasitic on his mate. The female's natural fishing rods attract smaller fish on which she feeds.

The cowfish, a variety of trunkfish, has an unusual triangular shape. Its body scales are fused, forming a solid shell around the fish.

Cowfishes may be over a foot long and are slow-moving swimmers because of their stiff bodies.

Common trunkfishes are somewhat smaller than cowfishes and are found mainly in waters off the coast of Florida.

tirely of reproductive organs. For the remainder of his life, the male is parasitic on the female, which may weigh a thousand times more than her mate.

The dorsal fins of the remora, or shark sucker, have been transformed into a suction disc by which the remora fastens itself to other fishes, thus hitchhiking its way through the ocean. It releases itself to feed on the scraps of food dropped by its host, which is generally a shark.

Blind goby fish of the Pacific hide beneath rocks, crawling about like slugs. A vicious little South American catfish lives in the gill chambers of other fishes, chewing at their gills and lapping up the blood that oozes out. Another fish inhabits the hollow, inner chamber of the sea cucumber, and still another spends its life in the midst of the dangerous tentacles of the Portuguese man-of-war. A colorful tropical fish of the West Indies lives inside the shell of a conch.

So even in the great expanse of water, fishes have definite "homes." Some of these homes are unusual places, while the exact limits of others are not as easily defined. Yet to the fishes these special niches are often vital to their lives.

Fish scientists have learned, for example, that when trout are taken from a hatchery and stocked in a stream a great many die within a few weeks. Often the only explanation is that the fish have not been able to find a place where they feel "at home" in the new water, even though it offers all the conditions necessary for their existence.

Using a suction disc on its back, the remora hitch-hikes a ride on larger fish.

Below, *a remora has attached itself to a leopard ray. Remoras are not parasitic, but eat crumbs from their host's meals.*

Above, *the dangerous stinging tentacles of the Portuguese man-of-war provide a safe home for one small fish.*

A sargassum fish, swimming near coral branches, is easy to see. In its natural habitat, however, the fish resembles the weeds so closely that it becomes almost invisible.

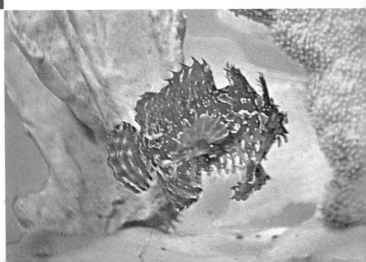

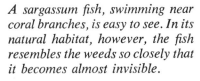

How Fishes Breathe

Since fishes live beneath the surface of the water, they cannot take oxygen directly from the air as land animals do. Instead, they breathe oxygen that is dissolved in the water. They do this by absorbing it through their gills.

Watch a fish in an aquarium. Notice how it is constantly opening and shutting its mouth as though it is drinking water. This is the way it breathes.

Each time the fish opens its mouth, water flows into its mouth cavity. And while its mouth is open, the gill covers, located on each side of the fish's head, are kept tightly shut. The fish's cheeks may actually puff out as its mouth fills with water. Then as soon as the fish shuts its mouth, its gill covers open, and the water inside is forced out.

When the fish is resting quietly, it gulps the water slowly. When it begins to swim or when it becomes excited, it opens and shuts its mouth more rapidly. Then it is "breathing hard," using up its oxygen at a faster rate.

Each gulp of water passes over the fish's gills, located just beneath its gill covers. These are a bright red color, for they consist of many thin-walled filaments where blood vessels lie almost exposed to the surface. Here the exchange of gases in the process known as respiration occurs. Carbon dioxide, the waste material carried by the blood, is given off and is carried away by the water that is forced out of the gills. At the same time, the oxygen in the water is absorbed by the blood and is transported to cells throughout the fish's body.

Different kinds of fishes do require different amounts of oxygen, and this often determines the sort of water in which they live.

Fish breathe by absorbing oxygen from the water through their gills. When the mouth is open, the gills are closed; then the gill covers open and water is expelled.

Trout, for example, need large amounts of oxygen. They can exist only in cold waters, which can hold a greater amount of absorbed oxygen than warm waters. In addition, the fast-flowing streams where most kinds of trout live are continually churning new supplies of oxygen into the water. In the sea, too, oxygen is more abundant in cold polar waters than in warm waters near the equator, and more is present when there are waves than when the sea is calm. Near the opposite extreme are many of the catfishes. They need much less oxygen for their survival, and so they can live in sluggish, warm waters in streams and lakes where the oxygen content is low. A catfish can remain alive for many hours when completely out of water. Carp also have low oxygen needs. By keeping them cool and moist, they can be shipped alive to markets far away.

Water is much less richly supplied with oxygen than air is. By comparison, air, with 21 percent oxygen content, contains 25 to 40 times more than an equal amount of water. Oxygen content of water also varies with the depth of the water and other conditions as well as with the temperature. For example, decaying plants use up oxygen and may reduce the amount available to fish. Sometimes this causes fish to suffocate in lakes and ponds—a condition known as summerkill. Blankets of ice and snow

Trout are found in cold, fast-moving waters which have a large oxygen content.

covering ponds and lakes in winter prevent plant growth and the churning in of oxygen at the surface. This may cause winterkill.

Oxygen is less abundant in deep water than near the surface, and may be completely absent in the depths of lakes or in the dark waters of the sea. As they manufacture food, growing plants give

Catfish need little oxygen, hence are plentiful in warm, quiet waters.

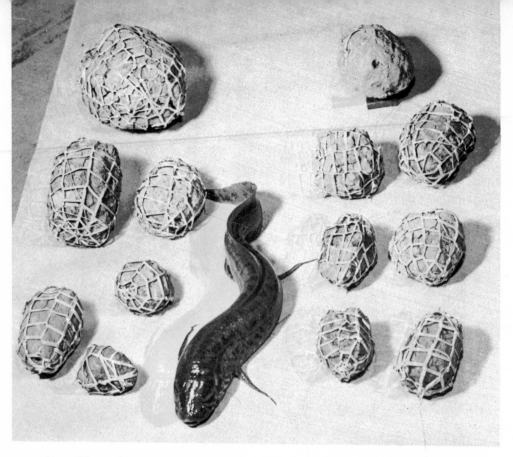

Lungfish can be shipped alive in their mud encasements. These primitive fish breathe air as land animals do and will drown if kept underwater too long.

off oxygen. So on sunny days, oxygen is most plentiful in the afternoon, and least abundant early in the morning. For these reasons, fishes may move from place to place, or be less active at certain times, in any body of water.

One of the most unusual fishes in the world is the lungfish, a native of the tropic regions of Africa, South America, and Australia. The lungfish can breathe air, just as land animals do. Its "lung" is its air bladder, which has been richly supplied with blood vessels. It connects directly to the fish's esophagus and from there to its mouth.

When a lungfish needs more oxygen, it comes to the surface and breathes a new supply into its lung. A lungfish will actually drown if it is kept underwater too long. In dry seasons, when the stagnant ponds where lungfish live dry up, these unusual fish burrow deep into the mud at the bottom. There they secrete a slimy protective coating around their bodies. They continue to breathe air through a small air hole that connects to the surface through the mud casing over them. When the rains come again and the pools fill with water, they emerge from these burrows.

18

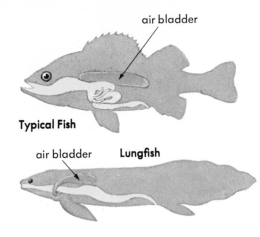

Typical Fish

air bladder

air bladder **Lungfish**

The "lung" of the lungfish is its air bladder, which connects directly to its mouth.

Another fish that can live out of water is the tropical mudskipper. Its gills are greatly reduced in size, but behind them in the fish's head are large, moist pouches containing many folds of tissue and numerous blood vessels. Air trapped in these chambers keeps the fish supplied with oxygen over long periods of time, and a mudskipper may spend more than a day without entering the water once.

On mud flats it "skips" about on its stubby, leg-like fins, chasing the crabs, insects, and other creatures on which it feeds. With a flip of its tail, it can leap as far as three feet. Or sometimes it rests on the bank or stretches out on a root while watching for its prey. At these times it hangs its tail in the water, for its tail is also abundantly supplied with blood vessels and can serve as a breathing organ, removing oxygen from the water in the same manner as gills.

These strange fishes that can breathe air, of course, are exceptions. The vast majority of fishes breathe with gills and are not able to live long out of water.

Mudskippers can breathe air and can move about on land, using their fins and tails as legs.

The Senses of Fishes

Most fishes are nearsighted. Since light cannot penetrate far in water, distance vision would not be useful to the ordinary fish. At close ranges, however, a fish can see clearly, especially moving objects.

The lens in the human eye is slightly curved. Furthermore, it is equipped with special muscles which can change its shape, thus enabling us to focus on objects that are close or far away. But the lens in a fish's eye is almost spherical, and its shape cannot be changed. Its focus is pre-set for near objects. A few species do have a muscle attachment making it possible to move the lens itself back and forth to get a sharper focus.

Typically, too, fishes have no eyelids. Their eyes are constantly bathed in water, and so they have no need for eyelids to keep their eyes moist, which is the principal function of our eyelids.

Some sharks, however, have three eyelids. In addition to the upper and lower lids, they also have semi-transparent membranes which move across their eyes. These lids, called nictitating membranes, work independently of the upper and lower lids, and the shark slides them over its eyes to protect its eyes from the sand, mud, and debris stirred up as it feeds at the bottom.

Since it has no eyelids, a fish cannot shut its eyes when it goes to sleep. And fishes do sleep—or rest—at regular intervals. Schools of perch, for example, scatter every night, and the fish drop down to the bottom individually to sleep. At daylight they assemble again in schools. Other fishes lie on their sides, while some sleep "standing up" or leaning against some object in the water. One eccentric fish dives into the soft bottom to take its naps. One of the tropical parrot fishes

Most fishes are nearsighted, but they have a very wide field of vision.

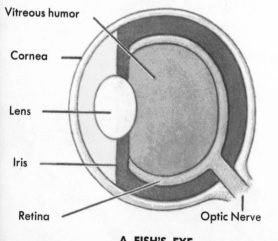

A FISH'S EYE

Vitreous humor

Cornea

Lens

Iris

Retina

Optic Nerve

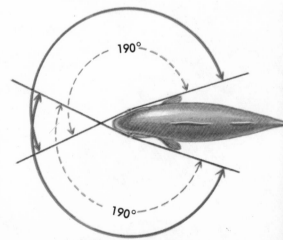

FIELD OF VISION

190°

190°

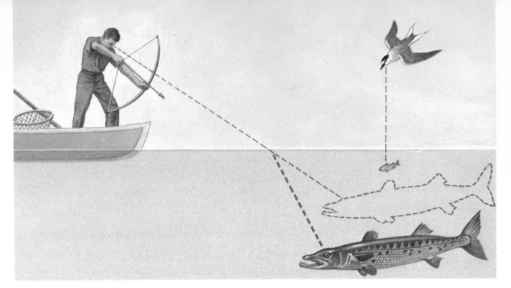

To the archer, the fish appears to be in a different place than it is, because light rays are bent as they pass from air to water. The bird, however, sees the fish in its true position.

secretes a mucous blanket around itself at night, often spending an hour or more every evening preparing its "bed."

What a fish sees when it looks from the water at some object in the air brings up an entirely different problem. Light rays travel at much greater speed in air than they do in water, which is more dense. Therefore, they are bent as they pass from air into water. This makes an object appear to be one place when it is really in another.

This is no problem for a fish-eating bird which dives on its prey from directly above, for as the bird begins its straight-down dive, the rays of light are also traveling on a straight path. The fish is located exactly where it appears to be. But if the bird makes its dive at an angle, it will miss its meal entirely unless it adjusts it strike for the bending of the light

The archer fish is an excellent shot and can hit a spider at a distance of several feet.

21

rays. Wading birds also have to take this into consideration.

Knowing this principle is sometimes important to a fisherman, too. He must have it in mind when he is trying to cast his bait or lure directly to a fish that he

*The four-eyed fish swims with its eyes half in and half out
of the water, thus it can see underwater and also into the air.*

sees in the water, or when he is trying to approach a fishing spot without being seen. It is even more significant, of course, in such sports as spearing or netting fishes or in shooting them with a bow and arrow. The fish is actually closer to the fisherman than it appears to be.

Sometimes fishermen wonder if fishes can really distinguish one color from another. Tackle-makers produce lures in a wide range of colors. A skeptical fisherman is likely to believe they are made solely for his eye-appeal rather than a fish's. Experiments indicate that fishes can definitely distinguish colors. Black bass, for example, can recognize red most quickly. Then green, blue, and yellow. There is a possibility, too, that individual fish prefer one color to another or that water conditions will at times make one color more recognizable than another.

The tropical archer fish is an outstanding example of a fish that has excellent vision. These strange fish actually shoot their prey by squirting pellets of water forcefully from their mouths. They are deadly accurate at distances up to four feet or more and can knock spiders from their webs, hovering insects from the air, or frogs from their perches on the bank. As the archer fish takes careful aim, it moves back and forth in the water to make certain of its range.

Another oddity in the fish world is the four-eyed fish. The four-eyed fish always swims on the surface of the muddy waters where it lives. Its bulbous eyes, located on the top of its head like a frog's, are half in the water and half out of the water. Although the four-eyed fish really has only two eyes, they function as four eyes because of their internal structure.

The lens in the eye of the four-eyed fish is egg-shaped rather than spherical. For vision in the water, light rays pass through the whole length of the lens; thus the four-eyed fish's vision in the water is as nearsighted as any other fish's. But when the four-eyed fish looks into the air, light passes through the short width of the lens. This gives the fish

Sharks have poor vision and depend on their sense of smell to locate their prey.

good distance vision for seeing objects in air. And since the four-eyed fish has no eyelids to keep its "air eye" moist, it dips its head into the water at regular intervals to wet its eyes.

The eyes of fishes that live in the deep, dark depths of the ocean are frequently greatly reduced in size. Fishes that inhabit the dusky regions of the sea, on the other hand, generally have enlarged eyes to utilize the small amount of light that is available. And fishes that live in the perpetual darkness of cave waters often have no eyes at all.

Fishes that have poor vision may make up for it by having a better sense of taste or smell. Catfish, for example, have poor eyesight, but they have "taste organs" distributed over their whole bodies. If a bit of food is held near a catfish's tail, the fish begins to open and shut its mouth, for it has tasted the food through its tail and is ready to eat. Catfish and some others have an acute sense of touch, especially in their barbels, the sensitive, whisker-like feelers. Sharks also depend on their good sense of smell to locate their food and will sometimes follow traces of odor for long distances through the sea to its source.

Many fish that live in dim ocean depths have big eyes while those that live in caves are blind.

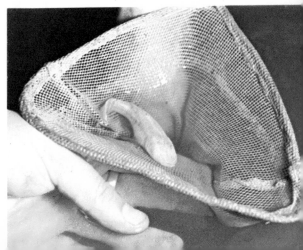

Some fishes, such as croakers, make noises that are amplified by their air bladders.

The nerve endings for the sense of smell are located in the fish's nostrils. These are blind openings at the tip of the fish's nose and are not used for breathing. An exception to this is the stargazer, which spends so much of its time buried in the sand or mud that its mouth is not usable in channeling water over its gills. The stargazer, instead, uses its nostrils for this purpose.

Most fishes can also hear noises and detect vibrations in the water. They will learn to come to a particular spot to be fed when certain sounds are repeated day after day at feeding time. Thus, the

Cross-section: bladder, pharyngeal teeth.

Amplified Air Bladder

Pharyngeal Teeth

ringing of a bell, the playing of the same music, the sound of a man's voice—all may become associated with food. Yet a fish has no external ears or ear openings. It does have a group of small bones which, in some fishes, function as ear bones, and since sound waves travel better in water than in air, a fish can hear noises even though it has no external ear opening.

In some fishes, these delicate bones are connected to the air bladder which then acts as a resonant chamber for sounds. Also, the fish's lateral line contains sensory cells, which open to the exterior through pores. With its lateral line, the fish can determine the direction of currents of water, detect the presence of nearby objects, and sense low-frequency vibrations. This is especially useful to a fish at night.

Finally, some fishes are far from being quiet creatures. They can make rasping, grunting, squeaking or squealing noises. There is even a catfish which can "mew." Some noises are made by rubbing together special bone extensions of the vertebrae. Others are made by vibrating muscles which connect to their air bladders. The air bladders amplify these sounds. Sound-detecting devices lowered into the sea during World War II to pick up sounds of enemy submarines were often "jammed" by the noises made by schools of fish. Often fish make loud noises when caught. This is particularly true of salt-water croakers and the fresh-water drum.

Fishes' Scales Tell Tales

An adult fish's body is covered by a protective coating of scales which overlap each other like the shingles on a roof. Outside these scales there is generally a thin, tight-fitting layer of skin containing glands that secrete a slime over the fish. This slime is a barrier to fungi, parasites, and disease organisms. To fishermen, of course, the slime is most noticeable because it makes a fish slippery and hard to hold.

The exposed portion of a fish's scale consists of a material which is much like our fingernails. Deeper in the skin there is a larger area of each scale, covered or overlapped by the scale behind it. The scale is alive, and it continues to grow throughout the fish's life. It pushes outward and enlarges as the fish grows bigger. Thus, the total number of scales on a fish's body remains the same throughout its life. New scales are added, however, to replace any that are lost through some mishap.

Fish scientists can tell much about a fish's past life by examining its scales. For one thing, they can determine its age. "Growth rings," much like the annual rings on a tree, appear on each scale as it increases in size. A heavy line separates the winter and summer seasons, for in winter, when food is less plentiful, a fish grows little or not at all. In summer, it is able to feed often and grows rapidly.

Between these most prominent lines, called checks, there are smaller lines that reveal other events in the fish's life. An expert scale reader can determine at what age a fish spawned for the first time, how often it has migrated, whether it has been sick, which years have been its best, and many such facts.

Tropical fish, which continue to grow at an even rate all year round, do not have summer and winter marks, but they do have firm lines showing the seasons of food abundance or shortages.

Counting the number of scales in rows on certain parts of a fish's body is a method used to distinguish one species of fish from another, even though the two may look much alike and are the same size. The common white sucker,

A fish's lateral line connects to sensory nerves and helps the fish detect vibrations in the water.

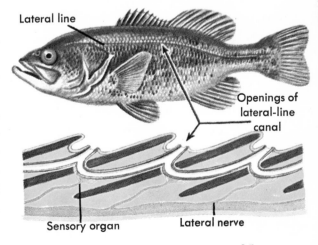

Lateral line

Openings of lateral-line canal

Sensory organ

Lateral nerve

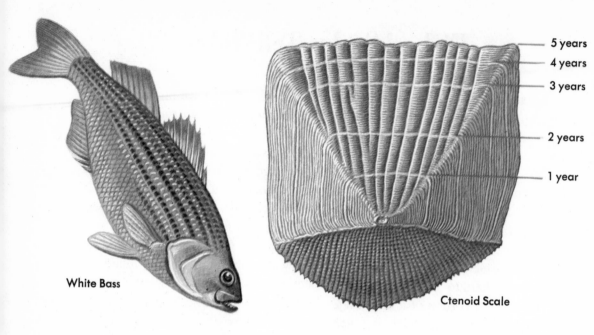

White Bass

5 years
4 years
3 years

2 years

1 year

Ctenoid Scale

*Fish scales have clearly defined growth rings
which can be counted to determine the fish's age.*

for example, has 80 or fewer scales in the row along its lateral line. Sturgeon suckers have more than 85.

Fishes do not have scales when they first hatch from the egg, but they generally appear within a few weeks. Catfishes never grow scales, however. They remain "naked" throughout their lives but are protected by their slippery skins and by the sharp spines, or horns, in their fins.

Paddlefish have no scales. Sculpins have few and generally modified scales, and mackerels have very tiny scales on their sleek, streamlined bodies.

Anchovies have large scales on their bodies, considering their small overall length of three to four inches, but they have no scales on their heads.

Swordfish have scales when they are young, then lose them as their long "bills" develop.

Trout have tiny scales that are covered with a thick skin, and an eel's scales are small, widely separated, and almost completely obscured by the eel's heavy skin. In contrast, the coarse, silvery scales of a tarpon may measure several inches across.

To determine the age of a fish which has small scales or no scales at all, scientists use other methods. They can count the "rings" on the fish's vertebrae. Similar "season" marks occur on the "ear stones," or otoliths, found in the skulls of bony fishes.

Garfish, one of the most primitive of our modern fishes, are covered with

26

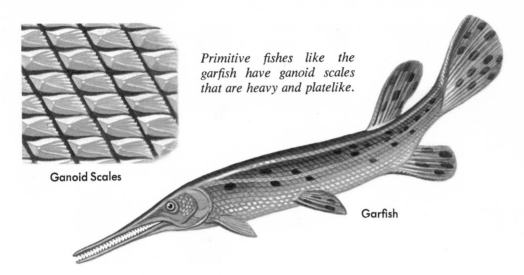

Ganoid Scales

Primitive fishes like the garfish have ganoid scales that are heavy and platelike.

Garfish

ganoid scales. These are hard, coated with enamel, and are laid down like the bricks in a walk. The ganoid scales of the sturgeon have become enlarged and shell-like, forming plates along the sturgeon's back and sides.

A shark has placoid-type scales. They are enamel-coated and have dentine cores, similar in structure to our teeth. In the sharks themselves this transition from body scales to teeth is easily observed. The scales are folded into the mouth and enlarged as teeth. If a shark breaks off its teeth in struggling with its prey, new ones begin growing in immediately. Sharkskin with its scales still attached is called "shagreen" and was once used to cover books, knife and sword handles, or for a sandpaper-like wood polisher.

The toothlike placoid scales of the shark are covered with enamel and have a dentine core.

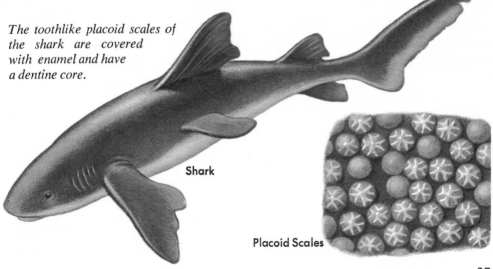

Shark

Placoid Scales

27

Some fishes change their colors by varying the amount of pigment in star-shaped cells called chromatophores scattered through their skin.

The Many Colors of Fishes

Many of our most familiar fishes are either silvery or chalky-white in color. This is caused by the deposit of a substance called guanin, a waste material of the blood, in certain cells in their scales. Sometimes these crystals of guanin act as prisms and break up the light that strikes them to produce metallic, iridescent hues.

But the actual colors of a fish—the blacks, greens, yellows, reds, and their combinations—are caused by special star-shaped pigment cells, called chromatophores. Many of these cells may be scattered throughout the fish's skin.

Some fishes change their colors as they grow older. Often they become darker with age as pigments accumulate.

Other fishes can change their colors to suit their moods or to match the background colors of their habitats.

These color changes are brought about when the fish varies the amount of pigment exposed in its chromatophores. Sometimes the pigment in a chromatophore shrinks so that only a small spot is still visible in a cell. At other times this same pigment may fill the cell. At one moment, then, a fish may be predominantly yellowish-orange in color, but as a black pigment spreads through its chromatophores, the fish's color will change first to a greenish hue, then finally to black.

Sometimes these color changes take place rapidly. They might occur as a fish moves from one type of background to another. Or a fish may flush with color at the sight of an enemy, as some male tropical fishes do when they see another male. Often the colors seem to ripple, changing from one to another. This may be a result of fright or shock, since it sometimes happens when a fish has just been caught. Salt-water dolphins put on an outstanding display of color changes when they are caught and brought up on the deck of a boat.

A frequently demonstrated example of a fish's ability to camouflage itself is

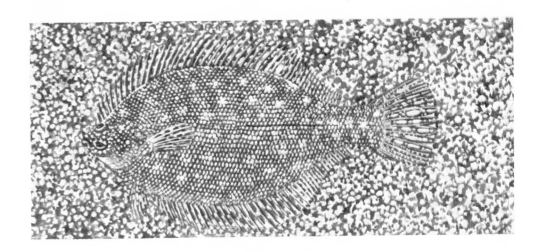

A flounder can match the fine-grained pattern of a sandy background (above) or can blend with the bolder pattern of larger rocks (below).

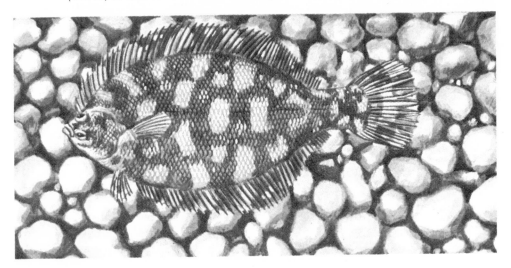

Many male fishes change their coloring during the mating season. The male fresh-water brook trout shown above have crimson throats and fins during the spawning season.

the flounder. In the sand, a flounder is a yellowish-brown color. But the instant it moves over a dark-colored bottom, its color changes to almost black. More spectacular, if the flounder swims into an area where the bottom is blotched with light and dark colors, the flounder itself becomes spotted. Experiments have shown that a flounder is so adept at matching the color pattern of its background that it can nearly achieve the square-checked pattern of a checkerboard. Nor is the flounder restricted to black, brown, and white. It can become reddish, yellow, green, or almost any shade to which it is exposed.

If a flounder is blinded, it loses this ability to match the color of its habitat. Thus, it depends on what it sees to know when and how to change its colors.

Male fishes sometimes become brilliantly colored at mating time. Some of the male fresh-water trout, for example, get crimson fins and throats as the spawning season approaches, and they remain brightly colored until the spawning season is over. After sockeye salmon leave the sea and begin swimming up fresh-water streams to their spawning grounds, the males get grotesquely hooked jaws and become dark red in color. Male bluegills have bright orange breasts at spawning time, and the mating colors of many minnows in fresh-water streams are almost gaudy.

In the deep waters of the sea, where there is no light, a majority of the fishes are black. Fishes of moderately deep waters—at the lower limits of light penetration—are typically red, while those in the upper lighted areas of the sea are generally blue or green. But fishes of warm coral seas display the greatest variation in colors and patterns.

30

A rock beauty swims through a coral forest.

Most colorful of all fishes are those that inhabit the warm waters of the coral seas. Shown above is a queen trigger-fish.

The striking markings of the tang fish identify this small inhabitant of tropic waters.

The brilliantly plumed lion fish of the Pacific and West Indies has sharp and poisonous spines on its back.

31

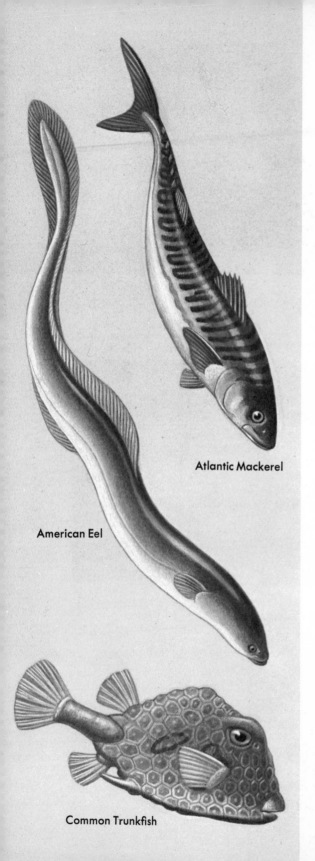

Atlantic Mackerel

American Eel

Common Trunkfish

How Fishes Swim

The shape of a fish's body often reveals its method of swimming.

Eel-like fishes, for example, wriggle the same way a snake does when it is crawling rapidly. Their bodies make a series of flowing "S" shapes as they move through the water.

A few kinds of fishes use only their fins for swimming. This is true of the trunkfish, for example, for its body is encased in a hard, shell-like covering, like a turtle. Only its fins and tail are movable. A trunkfish is neither fast nor graceful. Rays also use only their fins for swimming. By flapping their broad, wing-like pectoral fins, they literally "fly" through the water, like great water-borne bats.

All fishes use jet propulsion at times. This they accomplish by forcefully expelling the water from their gill openings and shooting forward. A flounder sometimes employs this method to explode from its place of concealment. By the time the silt and bottom debris stirred up by its sudden departure have settled, the flounder is out of sight.

But ordinarily we picture the sleek, streamlined body of one of the fast

Most fishes swim by moving their whole body from side to side; the Atlantic mackerel is an example. Eels wiggle their long bodies as snakes do, while the trunkfish can move only its tail and its fins.

Rays swim by flapping their large pectoral fins like wings.

swimmers, such as tunas or mackerels, when we think of a fish. Its torpedo-shaped body can slip through the water with little resistance. This is the shape frequently imitated by the designers of boats, airplanes, and automobiles in trying to achieve greater speed.

Beneath a fish's skin and scales there is a mass of W-shaped muscles arranged in segments. These muscles are actually the part of the fish that we eat. They are familiar to us as the "flakes" that separate from each other after a fish is cooked. When the fish was alive, they supplied the power which drove it through the water.

A fish's fins are typically used only as brakes or guides. They may also help the fish to "stand still" in the water, for its normal breathing tends to push it forward with a jet-like motion as water is expelled from its gills.

A typical fish swims, then, by moving its whole body from side to side. This is really the same snakelike movement used by eel-like fishes. In shorter-bodied fishes, however, the "S" shapes are incomplete and hard to see.

The mackerels, tunas, bonitos, albacore, and the closely related sailfish and marlins are among the fastest fishes in the sea. Some of them are believed to exceed 40 miles per hour. Many of these fast swimmers can fold their dorsal fins

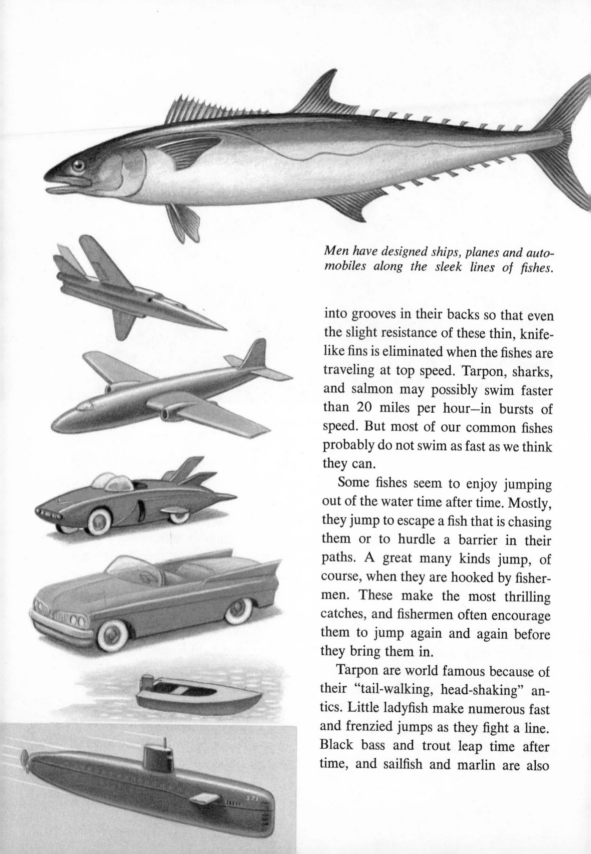

Men have designed ships, planes and automobiles along the sleek lines of fishes.

into grooves in their backs so that even the slight resistance of these thin, knife-like fins is eliminated when the fishes are traveling at top speed. Tarpon, sharks, and salmon may possibly swim faster than 20 miles per hour—in bursts of speed. But most of our common fishes probably do not swim as fast as we think they can.

Some fishes seem to enjoy jumping out of the water time after time. Mostly, they jump to escape a fish that is chasing them or to hurdle a barrier in their paths. A great many kinds jump, of course, when they are hooked by fishermen. These make the most thrilling catches, and fishermen often encourage them to jump again and again before they bring them in.

Tarpon are world famous because of their "tail-walking, head-shaking" antics. Little ladyfish make numerous fast and frenzied jumps as they fight a line. Black bass and trout leap time after time, and sailfish and marlin are also

Flying fish can glide long distances above the water on their winglike fins. They keep their tails in the water to propel themselves.

noted for high jumping. Mako sharks have been known to leap as high as the mast on a ship.

Sometimes a fish makes its jump by surging up from deep water. Others may be swimming close to the surface, then suddenly leap into the air. A powerful thrust with its tail gives the fish speed as it points its nose skyward.

Flying fishes have fins that are modified as gliding wings. With these "wings" extended they can soar for long distances over the surface of the water. Distances as great as a quarter of a mile have been reported. Now and then as it soars, the flying fish may drop close to the surface and submerge its tail, vibrating it rapidly to get enough speed to keep itself up in the air.

Once it was believed that a fish's tail was absolutely essential to the fish for swimming. Tails do vary greatly in size and shape, and many species undoubtedly get most of the driving force for swimming from their tails. But experiments have demonstrated that a fish can swim even after its tail fin is cut off. As

Tarpon, famous as game fish, are equally well-known for their vigorous leaps that carry them out of the water.

35

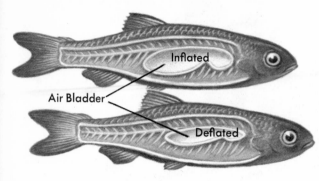

Air Bladder — Inflated / Deflated

By varying the amount of gas in its air bladder, a fish can make itself heavier or lighter so that it will rise or sink in the water.

a matter of fact, a fish soon learns to do without all of its fins if they are amputated. Steering and keeping upright in the water are difficult, however.

Sharks, which have poorly developed fins, can swim swiftly on a straight course, but they have trouble stopping and turning as compared to the bony fishes. Hammerhead sharks appear to use the broad extensions on their heads as rudders.

There are unusual methods of swimming, too. Sea horses, for example, swim in a "standing up" position, powered by wave-like movements of their dorsal fins. An African catfish always swims upside down. The head-stander swims with its head down and its tail up, and the pencil fish swims with its head up and its tail down. Needlefish and half-beaks skitter crazily across the surface with the front halves of their bodies held high out of the water and their tails still submerged, wagging rapidly, like a human swimmer treading water.

A fish's remarkable air bladder, which sometimes serves as a lung and sometimes as a sound amplifier, also assists it in swimming. By varying the amount of gas its air bladder contains, a fish can adjust its body weight to match the amount of water its body has displaced. This results in the fish having, in effect, no weight at all. So it will neither float nor sink but will remain suspended at whatever level it desires.

Flat-fishes do not have air bladders, and they sink directly to the bottom when they are not swimming. Sharks also have no air bladders. They have a tendency to sink, too, although the great amount of oil in their livers makes it easier for them to float.

Flounders and other flat-fish have no air bladders and sink to the bottom when they stop swimming. In some fish, air bladders are also used as a lung enabling them to breathe air, or as a sound amplifier.

36

How Fishes Feed

A typical fish is a flesh eater. Its mouth fairly bristles with needle-sharp teeth, and many kinds of fishes even have teeth on their tongues. Yet a fish does not chew its food as we do. It swallows its food whole, for its teeth are used only to grab and to hold its food or to bite off chunks of it.

Some kinds of fishes have no teeth at all. The sturgeon is an example. Long, fleshy organs, called barbels, hang down on the underside of the sturgeon's shovel-shaped snout. They brush against the bottom as the fish swims along. When these tasters touch a bit of food, the sturgeon's tube-like mouth, located behinds its barbels, immediately shoots out and sucks in the morsel.

The closely related, toothless paddlefish has a broad, flat nose in which there are numerous nerve endings. This highly sensitive proboscis is used to detect the almost-microscopic plants and animals on which the formidable-looking but entirely harmless paddlefish thrives. Strange as it may seem, the largest of all fishes—the whale shark—also feeds on small plants and animals, straining them from the water through its teeth, much as baleen whales do.

The toothless sturgeon sucks in its food through a tubular mouth.

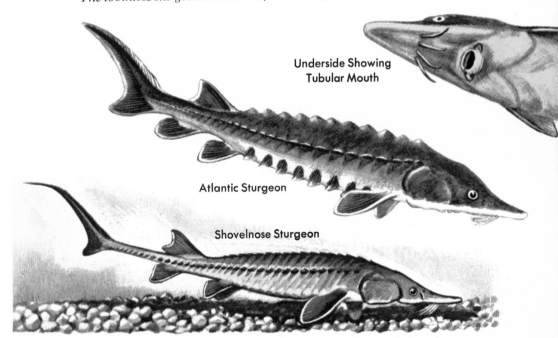

Underside Showing
Tubular Mouth

Atlantic Sturgeon

Shovelnose Sturgeon

Experienced fishermen adjust their lines on the level at which different fish feed.

Carp and suckers are both bottom feeders. They have small, toothless mouths, but their lips are thickened and protruded to form a sucking mouthpart. This is used like a vacuum cleaner to draw in small animals and plants from the bottom. Members of the minnow family have "teeth" in their throats to grind up the food they eat. Salt-water herrings also have pharyngeal teeth.

Catfishes, which have numerous small teeth and firm jaws, are not particular about what they eat. Their food can be alive, dead, or even decaying, and it is located largely by its odor, or taste. Since a catfish does not need to see its

38

food, it feeds mostly at night or in murky waters where it is hidden from enemies.

Many fishes have medium-sized teeth, such as those of the bass, bluegills, and other members of the sunfish family. These teeth are adequate for catching and holding average-sized prey, generally smaller than the fish itself. Northern pike and muskellunge, however, are real "tigers" of fresh waters. They have large, pointed teeth and will attack prey of any size. In salt waters, fishes such as sharks, bluefish, and barracudas are among the most fierce. One of the rays is frequently called the "clam cracker" because its flat, powerful teeth are used to crush oysters, clams, and other shellfish.

The teeth of the tropical parrot-fish are fused into a sharp parrot-like beak with which the fish bites off chunks of

The paddlefish has a long, sensitive nose.

coral. Swordfish and other members of the "billed" fish family have no teeth. Their mouths are like coarse sandpaper inside. It has been thought that these fishes may use their bills to stun their prey, then grab it and swallow it quickly. This theory is doubted by some scientists now, however. Sawfish have wide, saw-toothed snouts which are used similarly. And the vicious sea lamprey has a rasping, sucking mouth with which it bores a hole in other fishes, then draws out the fluids from its host.

Carp and suckers draw in small animals and plants from the mud at the bottom.

The long, thin muskellunge, a large, fresh-water fish 2 to 7 feet long, has many sharp teeth and a voracious appetite.

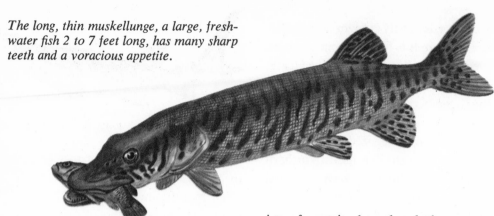

A number of fishes, such as the electric eels, torpedo rays, and stargazers, have organs which produce electricity, used to shock and stun their prey or to protect themselves.

Interestingly, a fish's digestive tract is also a clue to its diet. Fishes that eat only plants have long, coiled intestines—perhaps ten times or more the length of the fish itself. This is necessary because vegetable foods are more difficult to digest than is meat. Meat, which consists of protein, has already been processed once. Therefore, a flesh-eating fish has a short digestive tract. It is generally a straight tube and is no longer than the length of the fish's body.

Almost every body of water contains some fishes that eat plants, others that eat animals, and a few that are scavengers. A near exception to this is the deep sea, where nearly all fishes are carnivorous. Ordinarily, 600 feet is the maximum depth to which light penetrates the ocean with enough intensity to allow plants to grow. Below 1,200 feet, there is usually no trace of sunlight. Fishes

Some fishes have toothlike bones in their throats, called pharyngeal teeth.

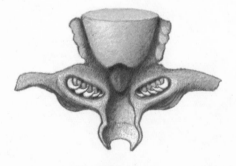

Pharyngeal Teeth
of a Tench

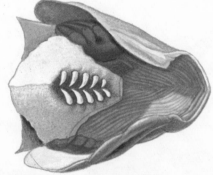

Pharyngeal Teeth Of a Barbel

that live in this black zone feed on each other and on dead and dying creatures that drift down from the lighted zones above them. Some kinds swim closer to the surface at night to feed.

Many of these deep-sea fishes have cavernous mouths and large, sharp teeth. The pelican fish even has a big pouch in which it carries its prey. The fins of others are elongated into "fishing rods" with luminous tips, or there are luminous organs over their bodies. These are to lure other fishes within their grasp or to identify each other in the dark depths.

Fish that live in the black depths of the oceans are all carnivorous, and many have wide mouths and long, needle-sharp teeth.

Great Swallower

Gulper

Vipertish

Prawn

Hatchetfish

From Egg to Full-grown Fish

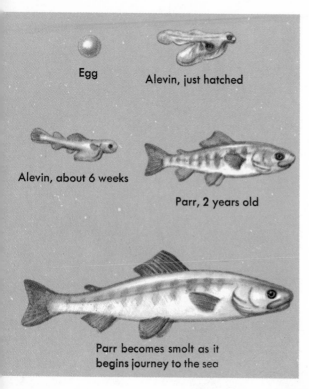

Egg

Alevin, just hatched

Alevin, about 6 weeks

Parr, 2 years old

Parr becomes smolt as it
begins journey to the sea

All fishes begin life by hatching from an egg. Some fishes lay their eggs in the open water. They make no nests and give their young no attention. They would not even recognize their own offspring if they saw them. Fishes of this sort generally produce large quantities of eggs, for the chances of survival of any one egg or young fish are extremely slim. In the case of some species, fewer than one of every 250 eggs survive.

Other fishes protect their eggs. The most common method is by building a nest and then standing guard over it until the eggs hatch. Sometimes one of the parents continues to watch over the young fish until they are large enough to

During the spawning season, the male sockeye salmon becomes a brilliant red.

female

male

yolk sac

The young of some species of sharks develop inside the mother and are born alive like the young of higher animals.

take care of themselves. These fishes generally lay fewer eggs. Their survival rate is much higher.

Still others give birth to their young. In fishes of this type the eggs are carried in the female's body until they have hatched, and then the young fishes are born alive.

Some species continue to carry the young inside their bodies even after they have emerged from the egg, and the young may receive nourishment from their mother. As a rule, fishes which give birth to their young produce the fewest number of offspring.

An exception to this are the rock-fishes, which may give birth to as many as 30,000 young at a time. Less than an inch long when born, these tiny fish are at first nearly transparent. They float about in the sea with the currents. It is several weeks before they acquire any pigment and begin to resemble the adult rockfishes.

Many of the sharks and rays also give birth to their young, and in some sharks there is a definite membrane attachment between the young and their mother that provides nourishment until they are born. Female rays sometimes leap high

The male toadfish guards the eggs. ▶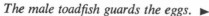

out of the water as they give birth to their young, a newborn being ejected into the water on each leap. Guppies, gambusias, mollies, and other aquarium fishes also give birth to their young.

Among fresh-water fishes, the bluegill is a good example of a nest-building species. As is common in the world of fishes, the male assumes a large amount of the responsibility for preparing the nest and then, after the eggs have hatched, guarding and caring for the young.

Males begin building their nests early in the spring, and since bluegills like company, a group of males select the same general area in which to make their nests. Each finds a spot that seems to suit his needs, and then he starts fanning the area with his fins. As he works, he turns his body first in one direction and then in another. Eventually, after much wriggling and sweeping, he has made a saucer-shaped depression in the bottom and has swept it clean of silt and loose debris.

Male catfish guard the swarming mass of newly hatched young.

As soon as the nest is finished, a female bluegill comes to lay her eggs in it. She lays an average of 5,000 eggs, although sometimes many more, and she may contribute to several nests during a season. As the eggs are laid, the male fertilizes them with a fluid called milt.

As soon as her eggs are laid, the female leaves the nest, but the male continues to hover over it. Frequently he fans the eggs, washing away any sand or silt that may have settled over them. At the same time, of course, he is stirring the water and keeping it fresh over the developing eggs. He also chases away inquisitive fishes that might eat the eggs.

After approximately a week, depending on the temperature of the water, the eggs hatch into a swarm of tiny bluegills. Still the male continues to stand guard over them. Several days pass before the young venture to swim away from the nest and not return. Then the male leaves, too.

Brook trout also build nests, but like other trout, they do not guard their eggs. The female trout is the nest builder. In a gravel area of a riffle, she begins making a depression in the bottom. The material she dislodges with her fins and body is washed away by the swift current. When the hole is several inches deep, she lays her eggs in it, and her mate fertilizes them. Then the female moves to the upstream side of the nest and begins dislodging more rocks and pebbles. They wash into the hole until it is filled.

The trout continue to work their way upstream, making more nests as they go. After several months, the eggs left in these nests hatch, and the young trout burrow out of the loose gravel.

Male bluegills build a nest, then guard the eggs, and later, the young.

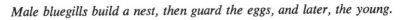

The male sea catfish shelters its young in its mouth, both before and after the eggs hatch.

two months, the male catfish eats no food.

Our common bullheads and many kinds of tropical fishes dig burrows in which they lay their eggs, and a female South American catfish carries her eggs attached to a spongy, adhesive disc on her belly. Common sticklebacks make neat nests of sticks and debris, much like a bird's nest, and the males defend these nests with their lives. Male gourami fish blow bubbles which stick together with the aid of a mucus secreted by the fish, and form a floating raft. Then the female lays eggs beneath the nest, and the male picks them up and blows them into the bubbles where they float about until they hatch. The watchful male always swims beneath the raft to chase away intruders. Siamese fighting fish also lay eggs in bubble rafts.

Some fishes give their eggs and young really unusual treatment. A male sea catfish, for example, carries the eggs in his mouth, which serves as a brood pouch. And after the eggs have hatched, he continues to carry the young fish until they are two inches or more in length. Sometimes they venture out, but when they are frightened, they dart inside to hide. All this time, of course, for about

The nest built by the male stickleback looks like an underwater bird's nest.

Brook Stickleback

male

Three-spined Stickleback

female in nest

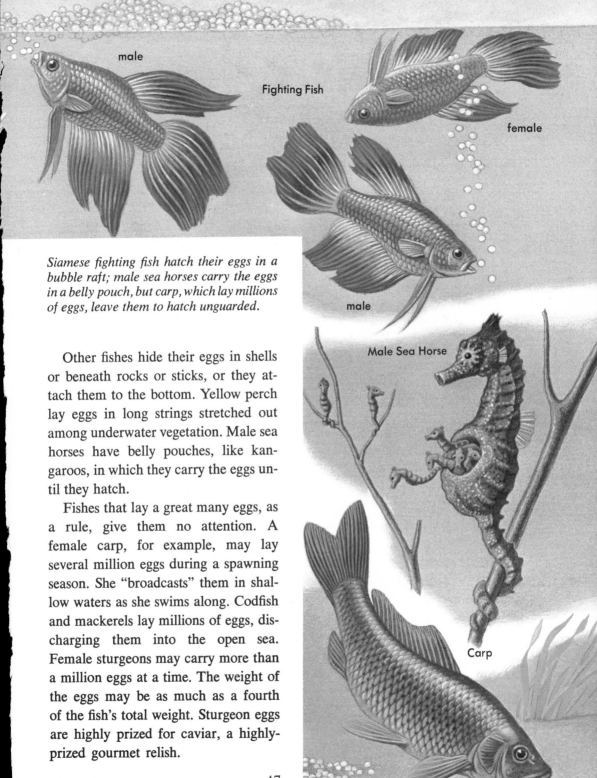

male

Fighting Fish

female

male

Male Sea Horse

Carp

Siamese fighting fish hatch their eggs in a bubble raft; male sea horses carry the eggs in a belly pouch, but carp, which lay millions of eggs, leave them to hatch unguarded.

Other fishes hide their eggs in shells or beneath rocks or sticks, or they attach them to the bottom. Yellow perch lay eggs in long strings stretched out among underwater vegetation. Male sea horses have belly pouches, like kangaroos, in which they carry the eggs until they hatch.

Fishes that lay a great many eggs, as a rule, give them no attention. A female carp, for example, may lay several million eggs during a spawning season. She "broadcasts" them in shallow waters as she swims along. Codfish and mackerels lay millions of eggs, discharging them into the open sea. Female sturgeons may carry more than a million eggs at a time. The weight of the eggs may be as much as a fourth of the fish's total weight. Sturgeon eggs are highly prized for caviar, a highly-prized gourmet relish.

47

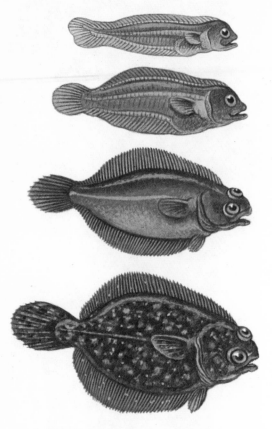

A flounder's eye moves as the fish grows.

Typically, a newly hatched fish, called a larva, still carries with it an undigested supply of yolk from the egg. This gives it a paunchy stomach, making it look much like a tadpole, but its built-in food supply gives it time to adjust to the outside world before it must begin hunting food for itself.

The time required for a young fish to mature varies greatly according to the species. Larvae of the sea lamprey live for as long as five years in fresh-water streams, generally buried in the mud at the bottom, before transforming into the parasitic adult stage. Baby bluegills, on the other hand, begin to resemble their parents within a few weeks and may have families of their own the following season.

One of the most unusual transformations made by young fish takes place in the flatfish family. A young flounder, for example, begins life by swimming in an upright position like any other fish. Its eyes are located one on each side of its head. Within a few days, however, the little fish begins to lean to one side. At the same time, the eye on the side toward which the fish is leaning begins to move to the other side. Within a month or two, the flounder is lying completely on its side, and its eye, too, has moved toward the top, migrating across the outer surface and finally stopping near the other eye, which is already on the side of the fish now uppermost.

Some flatfishes always lean to the left, others to the right, and still others in either direction, depending on how they get started. Also, the upper side of the flounder becomes pigmented, while the side toward the bottom is white.

Under natural conditions, few fish live a full life-span. As soon as age or disease begins to slow them down, they become easy prey for some other fish or for a fish-eating reptile, bird, or mammal. It is known, however, that some fish do live past the age of 50. Moray eels, common eels, and giant European catfish are some which have been known to live this long.

Fishes on the Move

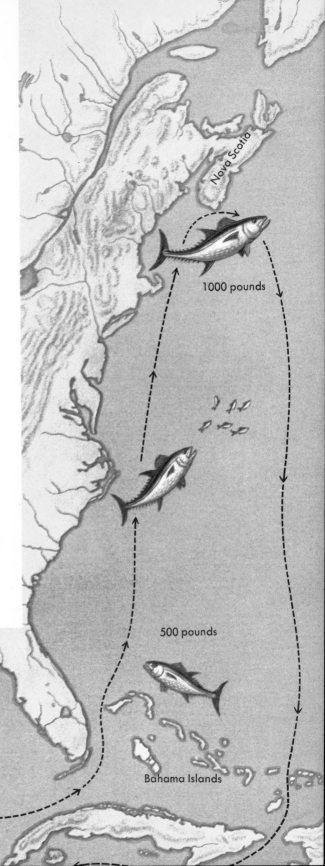

Many fishes have "homes" from which they rarely move during their lifetimes. Others are great travelers.

Some species move with the seasons. On the Atlantic coast, for example, the bluefin tuna journeys northward every spring following the Gulf Stream. Sport fishermen meet the great schools all along their route.

May is tuna fishing time in the Bahama Islands. Few of the tunas caught there weigh more than 500 pounds. But by August, when the tunas have reached Nova Scotia, they have doubled their weight, having stuffed themselves with menhaden, herring, and other food fishes along the way.

Bluefin tuna make a long migration beginning in the warm waters of the Gulf of Mexico, traveling up the Gulf Stream to Nova Scotia, and finally returning to the West Indies.

1000 pounds

Nova Scotia

500 pounds

Bahama Islands

Dolphins, tarpon, jacks, barracudas, and many other species drift northward in summer, then return to warmer waters again in winter. Other fishes, such as the codfish, come inshore to feed in shallower water in winter but return to deeper, cooler waters in summer.

Fresh-water fishes also follow their food and move about to keep themselves at a comfortable temperature. For this reason, some fishermen always take the temperature of the water at various depths and then lower their bait to the best level for the kind of fish they want to catch.

In summer, bass usually feed in shallow water early in the morning and again in the evening when they have a snack. But during the heat of the day they retreat to cooler, deeper waters. Perch, in contrast, feed most actively in the midday sun. In winter most fresh-water fishes retire to deep waters where the water temperature is fairly constant. There they remain less active until the following spring.

Many fresh-water fishes move to the headwaters of streams to build their nests and lay their eggs. Here the eggs can hatch and the young fish develop where their enemies are fewest.

Some salt-water fishes, in part of a most remarkable migration cycle, travel far inland to spawn in fresh water.

Salmon swim hundreds of miles from the sea to the headwaters of mountain streams to lay their eggs.

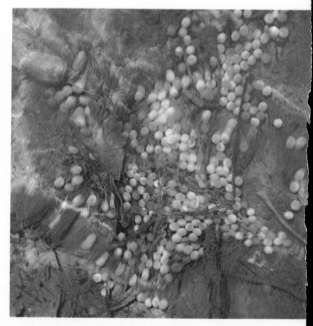

Born near the Sargasso Sea, eel larvae drift toward fresh waters in America and Europe.

King salmon, for example, may swim a thousand miles or more from the ocean to the headwaters of mountain streams to spawn. There, in gravel riffles, they lay their eggs and then die, too exhausted to make the return trip down the streams and rivers, back to the sea.

Shad, sturgeon, alewives, and smelt also travel from salt water to fresh water to spawn. But the common eel reverses the trip and journeys from fresh water to salt water to its spawning grounds.

For many centuries people had no idea where eels laid their eggs or for that matter, how young eels ever came into being. No one had ever seen a baby eel or an eel egg. Some people believed they came from horse hairs that fell into the water. Finally, a Danish naturalist learned the true story—and it is a strange one, indeed.

Both the American eels and the European eels, he discovered, spawn in the same area of the Atlantic Ocean. More specifically, near the Sargasso Sea. There each female lays millions of eggs, and the males fertilize them. It is believed that both adults then die.

Newly hatched eels are thin, transparent, and leaf-like. They are called

51

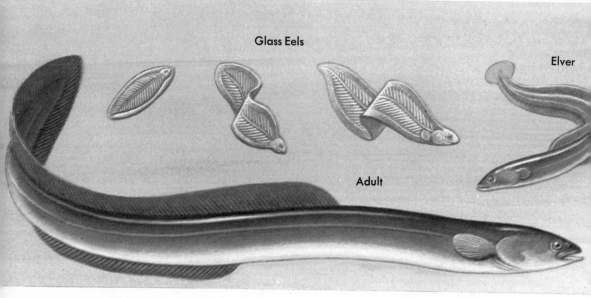

Glass Eels

Elver

Adult

In the thin transparent stage when they are known as "glass eels," the young eel larvae begin their long journey drifting from their salty ocean birthplace back to the fresh inland waters where they spend their adult lives.

"glass fish," and they do not resemble the adult eels at all. Drifting with the ocean currents, the baby eels soon begin their journey back to fresh water.

One of the most remarkable facts is that the young American eels come to North America and the European eels go to Europe—yet neither has ever been "home" before, and they have no guides to show them the way. For the American eels this is a trip of about 1,000 miles; for European eels, 3,000 miles or more. It requires nearly three years for the little eels to reach the coastal waters of Europe, while American eels make their trip in about one year. Yet the growth rates of the two species are so different that the young of each have developed to approximately the same size and maturity when they arrive in their "home" waters.

By this time the young eels are thicker-bodied and have begun to look much like their parents, in shape and coloring. Now they are called "elvers."

Male eels stay at the mouths of rivers and in coastal waters, while the females swim upstream. Occasionally, they crawl out of the water and wriggle through wet grass or marshes to get from one stream to another or to a lake or a pond. Eventually they settle down in one body of water where they feed and grow. Female eels grow to be three feet long or longer in their fresh-water homes. Males grow to be about a foot long.

52

After several years have passed, however, the eels' greenish-yellow color begins to fade. They turn almost white. Then they are known as "silver eels," and they are ready at this stage to begin their migration back to the sea to lay their eggs.

An equally extraordinary spawning run is made by the grunion, a small saltwater fish that lives in southern California's coastal waters. Grunion spawn approximately once every two weeks from March through June. Riding in on the waves of the highest tides of the full moon, just as the tide begins to ebb, they literally swarm over the beaches. Females, their abdomens swollen with ripe eggs, squirm into the wet sand. In pockets several inches deep, they lay their eggs, and males fertilize them. As the next high wave breaks over the beach, the fish wriggle into its fast-receding waters and disappear into the black sea.

The entire trip takes them perhaps an hour. Of this time only about a minute is required for the egg laying. And the timing is said by some to be so precise that the eggs are deposited on the very peak wave of the tide.

For nearly two weeks the grunions' eggs develop beneath the warm sands, but they do not hatch until they are bathed once again in salt water. Then the young grunions crawl out of the sand and swim out to sea with the tide.

The spawning grunion ride ashore on the crest of the tide, laying their eggs in sand pockets on the beach, and returning immediately to the sea.

Index

Photographs on p. 15 (top and center left), p. 31 (top left and right), by Russ Kinne; p. 23 (bottom left), p. 31 (center and bottom), by Cy La Tour, *Marineland of the Pacific;* p. 30, p. 44 (bottom), by W. T. Davidson from *The National Audubon Society;* p. 15 (center left), by William Schwarting of *The American Museum of Natural History;* p. 23 (bottom right), by Janet L. Stone; p. 45, Gene Hornbeck from *National Audubon Society;* p. 50, S. C. Wilson; p. 52, Richard A. Boolootian; p. 15 (bottom), p. 18, p. 33, New York Zoological Society.